THOMAS & FRIENDS™

Illustrated by S.I. International

Thomas the Tank Engine & Friends™

CREATED BY BRITT ALLCROFT™

Based on The Railway Series by The Reverend W Awdry
©2017 Gullane (Thomas) LLC.

Thomas the Tank Engine & Friends and Thomas & Friends
are trademarks of Gullane (Thomas) Limited. Thomas the Tank
Engine & Friends and Design is Reg. U.S. Pat. & Tm. Off.
© 2017 HIT Entertainment Limited.

Visit the Thomas & Friends website at: www.thomasandfriends.com

Published by Phoenix International Publications, Inc.

8501 West Higgins Road, Suite 300,
Chicago, Illinois 60631

Lower Ground Floor, 59 Gloucester Place
London W1U 8JJ

www.pikidsmedia.com

p i kids is a trademark of Phoenix International Publications, Inc.,
and is registered in the United States.

Look and Find is a registered trademark of Phoenix International Publications, Inc.,
and is registered in the United States and Canada.

8 7 6 5 4 3 2 1

ISBN: 978-1-4508-9753-2

phoenix international publications, inc.

PERCY

Thomas, Annie, and Clarabel have just arrived at Knapford Station to pick up passengers on their Branch Line. Can you find these items at the station?

ticket

train schedule

telephone booth

porter

clock

driver

GATE 1

TRAIN ARRIVALS

TRAIN DEPARTURES

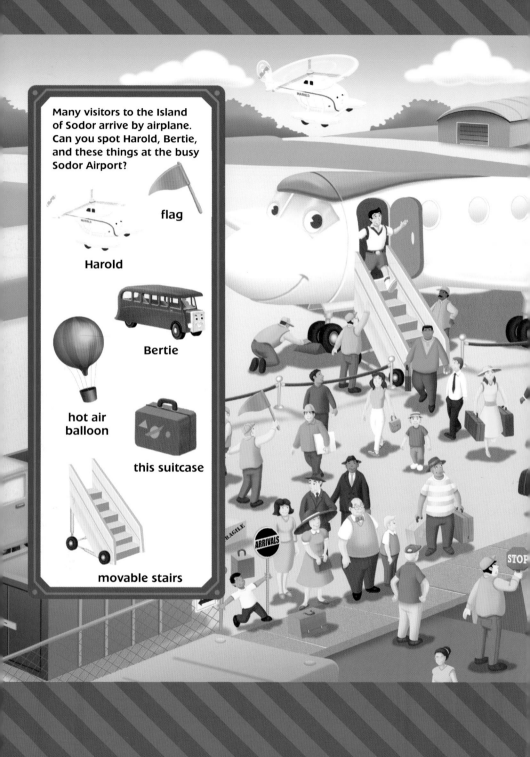

Many visitors to the Island of Sodor arrive by airplane. Can you spot Harold, Bertie, and these things at the busy Sodor Airport?

flag

Harold

Bertie

hot air balloon

this suitcase

movable stairs

Thomas is collecting fresh milk at Farmer McColl's farm. Can you spot these things on the farm?

ear of corn

rooster

cow

shovel

scarecrow

Terence

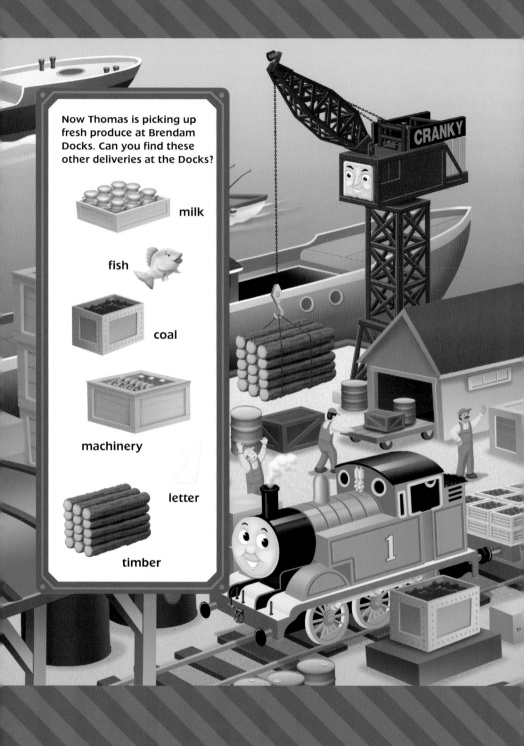

Now Thomas is picking up fresh produce at Brendam Docks. Can you find these other deliveries at the Docks?

milk

fish

coal

machinery

letter

timber

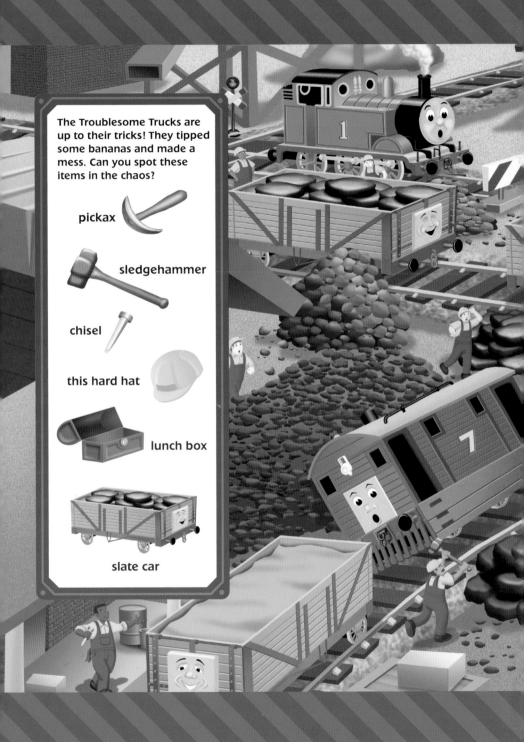

The Troublesome Trucks are up to their tricks! They tipped some bananas and made a mess. Can you spot these items in the chaos?

pickax

sledgehammer

chisel

this hard hat

lunch box

slate car

The circus has come to Sodor! Thomas is delivering supplies to the Fairgrounds. Can you find these parts of the circus celebration?

show dogs

this performer

barker

peanut vendor

trapeze artist

barbells

Thomas is at the train yard waiting for Sir Topham Hatt to finish his lunch. Take a peek in the office and see if you can find these items:

telephone

Lady Hatt

pocket watch

top hat

handkerchief

map of the railway

It's a great day for the seaside. Thomas gets to carry his favorite passengers — the children of Sodor! Can you find these items?

this blanket

ball

kite

ice-cream cone

sand sculpture

balloon

TRASH

Knapford Station is buzzing with people bustling about. Can you find these items that passengers have left behind?

glove

eyeglasses

apple

flowers

red coat

umbrella

People are coming from far and wide to the Island of Sodor, and the airport has never been busier! Can you spot these visiting vacationers?

woman wearing a yellow sun hat

man wearing a white vest

boy on a bicycle

woman carrying a picnic basket

girl with a tennis racket

man eating an ice-cream cone

Farmer McColl grows a rainbow of fruits and vegetables. Go back to the farm and find these other colorful things:

red wheelbarrow

orange peppers

Farmer McColl's yellow hat

green rake

purple eggplants

gray horse

There is always plenty to do at Brendam Docks. Can you lend a hand and find these useful vehicles?

barge (Bulstrode)

diesel train engine (Salty)

crane (Cranky)

cart

fishing boat

bus (Bertie)

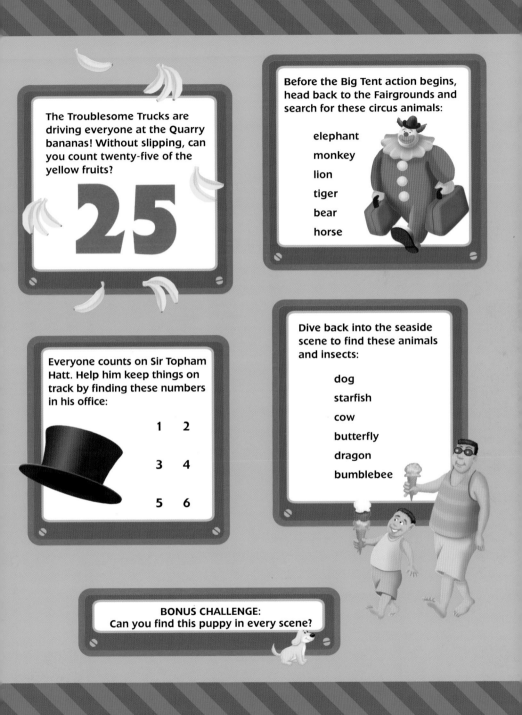

The Troublesome Trucks are driving everyone at the Quarry bananas! Without slipping, can you count twenty-five of the yellow fruits?

25

Before the Big Tent action begins, head back to the Fairgrounds and search for these circus animals:

elephant

monkey

lion

tiger

bear

horse

Everyone counts on Sir Topham Hatt. Help him keep things on track by finding these numbers in his office:

1 2

3 4

5 6

Dive back into the seaside scene to find these animals and insects:

dog

starfish

cow

butterfly

dragon

bumblebee

BONUS CHALLENGE:
Can you find this puppy in every scene?

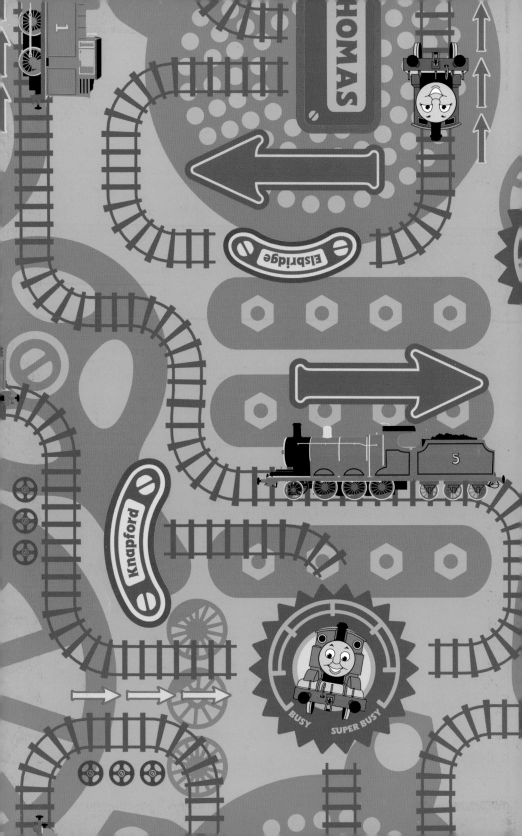